Jimmy Bauter

Gaia Holmes.

William Thirst-Gaskill

'By putting emerging writers alongside some of the biggest names in contemporary literature, Grist provides a unique opportunity for those starting out as writers.'

SIR PATRICK STEWART

WE'RE ALL IN IT TOGETHER

poems for a

disUNITED KINGDOM

Edited by
MICHAEL STEWART,
STEVE ELY &
KAYLEIGH CAMPBELL

GRiST

We're All In It Together:
Poems for a DisUnited Kingdom
is published by Grist Books

www.hud.ac.uk/grist

ISBN: 978-0-9563099-2-1

Grist Books is supported by the University of
Huddersfield and Arts Council England.
We would like to take the opportunity to express
our gratitude for this continuing support.

Editor-in-Chief: Michael Stewart
Cover and text design: Peter Barnfather

Printed and bound in Great Britain
by Imprint Digital, Upton Pyne, Exeter.

Contents

Preface

We're All In It Together has its origins in an earlier Grist project, edited by our former colleague in the department of Creative Writing at Huddersfield, Simon Crump. Simon had planned two anthologies of political and protest writing. The first, focusing on the short story, was published as *Trouble*, in 2019. *Strife*, the second anthology, was to be focused on poetry and was scheduled for 2020 publication. Unfortunately, a range of factors, not least Simon's departure from the University, combined to prevent the book from being produced. After a short delay, the current editors took on Simon's project, reshaping it from the protest politics of *Strife* to the broader, 'state-of-the-nation' focus of *We're All In It Together* – the title, of course, being taken from the disingenuous Tory slogan first used by Chancellor of the Exchequer George Osborne, in introducing the first of a decade of austerity budgets in 2010, and recycled endlessly by Conservative prime and cabinet ministers, leader writers, client journalists and right-wing fellow travellers since. The new project also differed from *Strife* in that it proposed to include commissioned poems from established poets alongside poems generated from the open call:

The United Kingdom of Great Britain *&* Northern Ireland
is a post-imperial state that has failed to adapt to its reduced
role and status in the world and with the history and legacy
of empire. The fault lines of national and regional identity,
and of class, race and gender continue to be significant obstacles
to the development of a meaningful sense of unity, and the
devolution of society into digital solipsism and consumer
narcissism is feeding the development of individualism and an
increasingly atomised society. The national rupture precipitated
and exposed by Brexit has thrown our divisions into stark
relief: on one side, triumphalism, hostility, gloating and a

will to dominate; on the other, hopelessness, sadness and only fragmented protest and resistance. Yet both 'sides' seem to be characterised by an underlying confusion and a lack of confidence about values and purpose in the context of national identity and the role and nature of the State. Meanwhile the world continues to globalise with the Neo-Liberal model overwhelmingly dominant, and the ecological crisis of the Sixth Extinction intensifies. What does it mean to be 'British' in this apocalyptic context? Is it possible for the Kingdom to become United? Is it even desirable? Or was that unity always a fiction – in Benedict Anderson's terms an 'imagined community'? *We're All In It Together* is an anthology that looks to explore these issues and we're looking for you to contribute your poems or hybrid pieces. We're not looking for any particular type of poetry or, indeed, any particular type of politics. Interpret the brief in your own way.

When the poems began to arrive (over 400 of them), the editors were immediately excited by the energy and quality of much of the work submitted, but it soon became apparent that not every poet had found it easy to adapt to the theme. In many instances, we encountered submissions from poets whose names we recognised – published poets, well-known on the scene, writers we admired – only to find the poems they had submitted didn't quite hit the mark because their arguments, characters, situations and images were too on-the-nose, and the tone too hectoring and didactic. The social media echo chamber of liberal and middle-class Remainers rang loud in poems that blamed Brexit/ Broken Britain on shaven-headed, tattooed, pit bull owning, lager-drinking white van men, or the amazingly prevalent used-car salesman brother-in-law. Other poems read like mansplaining *Guardian* op-eds, and not a few seemed to be written from the verandas of second homes in Tuscany or Provence. It is unsurprising that the shadow of Brexit loomed large in submissions. What was surprising was the lack of subtlety and nuance in many of those submissions – and the troubling othering and stereotyping of the white working class that manifested. Perhaps the *kulturkampf* nature of contemporary political discourse, combined with the dominance of the first person, personal lyric in the middle-class world of contemporary British poetry, has atrophied our sense of the well-judged public or political poem?

Thankfully, plenty of poets came at the theme sideways, demonstrating originality, boldness and flair alongside subtlety and insight. The poems that addressed the theme most effectively were the ones that presented a striking or ingenious image/series of images without providing commentary or drawing conclusions for the reader, or which otherwise surprised, excited and delighted us with the usual qualities of the 'good poem' – lexical virtuosity, skill with form *&* structure, deftness, humour, distinctiveness of approach and a reflexive refusal to flinch when dealing with contested or controversial subject matter.

What follows then, is an anthology that includes poems from a range of writers: from established poets with national and international reputations, to poetic first-timers and everything in between. Although it was disappointing that submissions from men outnumbered those from women by four-to-one, the editors feel that the diversity of the writers included has resulted in a pleasing diversity of approach – and an anthology that is variously dazzling, exhilarating, thought-provoking, laugh-out-loud funny – and at times, a bit of a grenade.

On a final note, it is perhaps fitting that *We're All In It Together* emerged from *Strife*, as the unity, solidarity and commitment to justice implied in the former only emerges from the struggle implied in the latter. You don't just pluck the golden apple from the tree. Which brings us back to Simon Crump and the Sheffield tree protest. This anthology is dedicated to him.

Michael Stewart, Steve Ely,
Kayleigh Campbell *&* the Student Team

WE'RE ALL IN IT TOGETHER

Poems for a DisUnited Kingdom

Imperial Exodus

Jim Greenhalf

I.

Did you see it, the last boat leaving?
Thank God they've gone. Good riddance.
All those years they've been telling us
what to do and how they want it done.
Things can only get better now, they say.
No more Pax this and Pax that.
When was the last time we did anything
out of order? That's what they've done to us.
The light will be purer now that its gleam
is unsullied by blood and eagles in their arenas.
And they called us barbarians!
They treated us as refugees in our own country:
changing our habits, our customs, words;
taking our women; thrusting themselves at us
like belly-piercing swords.
We paid for their empire, did their dirty work,
served as auxiliaries, while they tossed off
in their hilltop summer villas.
Why did we let them do it for so long?

II.

Well, that's that then. Four centuries
of empire in our wake. Down the hole.
I'm sorry to be going back.
Nothing glorious in that old ruin
of slaves and foreigners,
pouring like floodwater over our borders.

Were we too dependent on them
to keep our way of life in order?
They said they were serving us,
but weren't they also serving themselves?
They knew we hadn't the money
to pay for our armies at home and abroad.

Fiddling, corruption, laziness, cowardice:
did we civilise the world for this?
We, who stand on the shoulders of
indomitable men of steel and marble?
I'll piss in the cup and pour a libation
on the head of any fat, pontificating fool,

beating out the rhythm of our decline
like some mad *hortator*, dragging us back
to that bargain basement of fools and whores.
They won't survive; without us to protect them,
they'll be eaten alive by jackals and wolves.
Too late for warnings. Do you think we'll be missed?

Rachael From Swindon

Ben Willems

They're going to work on Rachael from Swindon.
This is the Corbyn shakedown. This is the proverbial
Orgreave truncheon, class conjunction.

She's on a list with Damo and Red Til I'm Dead.
All you curtain twitchers, clothes line snitchers.
Dirt. Dirt. Going through bins like a Russian accessory.

She's from Swindon but it could've been Warrington.
Milkshake mardy in a Barratt home box room.
She's Jennifer Aniston meets Ricky Tomlinson.

While you were channelling Del Boy and Frank Spencer
the TV stars got older. Many ballbag Alan Sugar.
All the fakes rinsed out fake in the food bank queue.

Marcus Rashford. Social welfare. 21.
The fence patrollers are losing their collective Ronseal shit.
Blacklist! What??? You can't blacklist Marcus Rashford!

FFS think about it. Make it about her trainers.
Implied lifestyle. And who gives her that platform?
Voices of the humdrum towns. Speak up wet verges

for the real gutter press.

Strandline

Gaia Holmes

The word sounds like a blessing,
like the name of a flower, like Melissa
or Alyssum, like something that 'gives':
pollen to the bees, a lullaby, a warm lamp
in the window of a harbour house.

When did it start to mean
too many shivering bodies
crammed into the freezing black
of a refrigerated lorry? When did it start to mean
overcrowded skiffs and flimsy dinghies,
women singing through the spume
to their damp and bluing babies,
desperate people making their own moons
with their mobile phones, hoping
that some kind, fat-lunged god
will blow their boats across the border?

From the Greek meaning
a 'refuge' or 'sanctuary',
meaning *soup* and *safe* and *welcome*,
meaning *here is some tea and bread,*
here is a bed for you to lie on.
Now the word seems to have lost
some of its softer meaning.

More a word of law than a word
of instinct and reason, meaning
bills and *clauses*, meaning *border control*
and the rude muscular beams
of searchlights scoring the water, meaning
cold strip-lit holding rooms and melamine tables,
bad coffee in Styrofoam cups and forms and questions
and questions and forms and BLOCK CAPITALS ONLY
and DO NOT WRITE OUTSIDE THE BOX,
meaning *hostels* and *limbo* and *stigma*.

The word is an island that's hard to reach
and most mornings on its beaches
there are water-logged trainers,
sodden passports and Save Our Souls,
among the beer cans
tangled in seaweed, lost names
and bright unfinished lives
fading on the shingle,
a different kind of flotsam
on the strandline.

Fresh off the Boat

Safia Khan

It is night when the boat starts to sink –
not enough life jackets.
He gives the last one to his sister
who clutches his leg, his body a raft.
By the time he makes it to shore,
her lungs are full of salt and ice.
He holds her limp body all night
as they sway in the van like cattle.

It is night when he stands frying chicken
in the back of a shop for rowdy teens
tanked up to the brim on White Lightning.
They spit out his country on a list of places
they think the UK should invade,
to the soundtrack of golden oil splashing.
He smirks, they are so drunk
they don't realise they already have.
His boss flashes a traffic light eye,
reminds him of his pending status.

It is day when I teach the proper vocab
for clothing. His eyes are nets,
catching what swims at them, his hands
driftwood when he holds out a phone,
asks please if I call him sometime.
I can't, I'm only his teacher. He nods.
It's just I have same name as his sister,
and this country is cold, and my voice
is like, and he points to the board,
blanket.

Omni

Ian Duhig

William Barnes proposed that we call buses
'folkswains', which sounds folk kitsch, or even völkisch.
'Bus' has stuck: from 'omnibus': 'for all',
for us – kin to 'omnium-gatherum',
a ragbag, like Leeds and this ragtag bin
of labyrinthine thoughts from my home since
its 'Motorway City' days – a maze then,
but *the* place to get your threads made. No more,
its tailors' chalk and pins are history;
our rag trade's gone for a Burton, a phrase
from Leeds terse talk which Tony Harrison
thought naturally fell into blank verse –
that term suits me well: my mind's often blank:
I'll lose the thread, bear no comparison
with Calvino's Ersilians who wound
their threads through city streets to indicate
relationships with colour-coded clues
and weave their state into a life-size text
of unity until, like refugees
from whom they'd grown, their interpersonal
complexities, they'd rise and leave as one
to found their next Ersilia elsewhere.
The UK's imagined community
has nowhere else: it snapped the threads that mapped
its maze and gets lost following its bent
or buses with big lies along their sides.
Reflecting its predicament therefore,
its ruling chaos, U-turns, disarray,
by public transport or on Shanks' pony,

with connections missed, timetables spurned,
lines crossed, I'll dérive, veering here and there,
digress and stray – so think straight away
of Leeds Surrealist, Tony Earnshaw
(worked in engineering: more threads stripped),
who skipped from bus to train as chance might link,
unstitching what fixes how we see Leeds.
Now, from outside the library where Earnshaw
learned his new trade, art (not cyber-y),
I start my Earnshavian state-of-the-nation
hack waiting at the stop for 36s,
red and black as Tony's anarchism,
like John Quail's, the movement's historian
who I knew at Leeds Federated
Housing Association. They'd house the needy,
will do now, when capital allows
(others in that game are just greedy blight-
ers). My bus has come through Gledhow: 'kite hill' –
'gled' still means kite in Scots, proverbially
greedy; we lost the word, Scotland too –
maybe Northern Ireland, Wales the same.
The UK cannot hold: its centre's sold,
anarcho-capitalist appetites
are fed: new kites turn in widening gyres
above our local hospital, school, library …
The 36 aspires to 'libraries' –
in truth, a shelf for passenger donations
where, from duty, I left a Sterne myself,
being grateful for good wi-fi and the joys

of writing while being carried through green beauty –
"Poetry's not born in noise, in crowds,
or on a bus. There have to be four walls ..."
Szymborska's wrong here: Brodsky's nomad song
of poetry opposed to settlers' prose
gets closer to the truth. I ride today,
but not through God's Own Countryside: to town,
by sites of knocked-down pubs, the lost Hayfield
whose wall once read 'REMEMBER OLUWALE',
Empire migrant who learned its 'family' lie,
the cost of this tuition being his life.
Both pub and wall are gone, but those words hang
in the air. Some of us remember him,
in different ways, with poetry and plays
from many hands, steel plaques, steel bands –
I saw here, during Carnival, King David
dance again with 'migrant masqueraders',
raising spirits: crowds, street traders, mine, his.
In my mask now, I see we're near the house
of great folk musicologist Frank Kitson;
I bow to him and those whose songs he saved,
a working class still told their culture's rank,
their dignity a joke. No shock some broke
ranks, hearts, traditions. I wish them all well
and those who lied to them cold Hell. We pass
the Roscoe's site next up, old Irish pub
where I could hear Ó Catháin sing sean-nós,
a style since Petrie linked with India –
how Satnam Galsian renders the air,

She Moved Through the Fair proves he had a point.
For more signs of the Jewel in the Crown,
I cut back down to board a 99
that runs by closed-down stations and lost lines,
but can afford from its top deck a view
into a garden with Ganesha's statue,
tusk snapped off, replacing the pen he broke
in taking Vyasa's epic dictation
of the *Mahābhārata*, greatest poem ...
Divine Reprover of my Sloth, I pray
Ganesha, O Obstacle Remover:
no poet needed you as much as me;
no country needed you so much as this!
But, silently, Ganesha waves goodbye.
Near fields of rotting crops, I spot a park
where lorries come to cark like elephants
then, up the ridge, beneath a creaky bridge,
the Wharfe, where weeping kings nurse seeping thighs,
and turn their leaky fishing boats in rings
beneath thin skies we're burning off like dew,
above a sea too high for us each year,
too near to where flood walls could fail again.
The bus pulls in to Wetherby too late,
Bielsa's terminus, Kop god. Once seen
in local restaurants, the coffee shop,
he'd sign each autograph with patient grace,
where I'll swill ale with mangelwurzel pie
for half a groat, or will do in some future
heaven of folkswain Merrie Englanders,

with Pearly Kings, Faerie Queens, Emperor
Boris clothesless ... Early for the 7,
time allows a visit to the arch
of Huguenot réfugiés, inscribed
'Aimez votre prochain comme vous-même'.
A martyr to his anal fistula,
the Sun King exiled them: I could say too,
'L'état, c'est moi', in my state all at sea
with refugees from who they really are.
Believe: their past's a lie they've long been sold,
a foreign country with its borders closed.
Old Huguenots could train us to reweave
the national tapestry, tie in rogue threads,
not hide a stain but set it in the pattern –
were we open to real history:
for most, that's country miles too rational:
surrealism's now a better guide
and Tony Earnshaw's ghost smiles at my side.

Codenames

Ashley Hickson-Lovence

there's an old shop in Norwich that sells
board games but doesn't accept card

it's on Elm Hill, a little cobbled street
considered by many, to be
the most beautiful in the city

went in the other day
took a fancy to *Codenames*
which is all about connections *&* connotations
& making links between seemingly disparate things
played it once in Godalming
came up with the clue 'Aeroflot'
to link the words 'Russia' and 'Trip' together

I'll take it, I said, but did I have the cash? (does anyone?)
there I am, looking for coins
digging out the pennies
fishing for pounds
trying to get to sixteen
pushing index finger in
fingering the copper
displaying no shortage of effort

but there *has* been a shortage of petrol recently
& I don't want to be a prick
so I'm not going to panic
buy, even though I'm panicked
about how I will get to work in the morning

most days I write words & read the works of others
still to work out the difference
between a side hustle and a proper career
there's no shortage of ideas
up here, top-floor Travelodge
staring at the suspect stains
slurping Hazy Janes
but there is a shortage of:

bouncers and bar staff / GPs / grassroots football referees /
carbon dioxide / test tubes / HGV drivers / asparagus pickers /
carers / Christmas turkeys / crisps in Co-op / compassion

there *is* a little boy, eight or so, who's been caught short
pissing into the wind on the hard shoulder of the M11

there's no lack of talent in the classrooms
in Hethersett or Woodberry Down or Wood Green
there's no shortage of care
from the Crocs-wearing nurses
working stupidly long shifts
& clapping won't pay their bills or soothe their migraines

there's no shortage of distrust, disgust and disdain
& politicians proving as useful as a speed camera in traffic
& as insufferable as rubbing an itchy eye with a dirty finger
& I'm still here, digging in
getting in the cracks and crevices
trying to retrieve every last penny
I might just have enough to pay, just enough to play
but it's not been easy
& now we have nothing left

Heritage
Joelle Taylor

it is said when they opened him
they found a coal mine in his chest
& inside the mine, tiny men
hacked at the black
their helmet lights nattering
Morse Code, sticky with dialect
his blood, bad traffic
his lungs, blackbirds lewd-whistling
and that is not a tongue
that is bunting
& the smaller man over there
balanced at the pit head
that is his son –
boy stubbed
shout boy –
& if you opened him
you would find a swarm of fists
nesting in his chest
which shout boy
hand-reared on strips of
housey housey, going to the dogs,
and Littlewoods catalogues
rain as hard as the gossip
that congregates around the head
of the smallest
of daughters
it is said that if you opened her
you would find
a departure lounge in her chest

& a long line of coughing ghosts
queuing quietly
passports in red
& bruise
& white.

o' I pulled a bingo hall from my chest
o' I pulled out a family of four
o' I pulled a drop-leaf dinner table from my chest
o' I pulled out England.

Another Debate in My Parent's Kitchen

Kayleigh Campbell

My mother is an island.
I've stood at her shorelines

in biting winds,
ready to drift out with the tide.

I've driven miles, in search of her
heart, what she hides in its chambers.

I've scoured for tumours, for trauma
points – for explanation.

I've clawed through the earth of her
brain, looking for miswiring roots.

I've dropped to my knees on
the heathland of her chest.

My mother is an island
I can't bring myself to leave.

Reversible, Halts
MacGillivray

By 1961, poet Kristján Norge became convinced that he was, in fact, a demon. Subsistence on the Hebridean island of Dubhan had become an increasing strain for Norge, who felt his exiled status intensively. In response to both this isolation and the sudden revelation of his demonhood, Norge embarked on creating an amnesiac system, convinced that if he could forget himself, then redemption might follow. Enormously flawed, the system has only been recovered in fragments, scratched out in notes and excerpts of lines that sometimes constitute poems, but more often comprise conflicted jottings. Apparently, Norge's conviction that Dubhan contained a thin skin, or portal, through which he had been washed up, leant weight to the idea that Dubhan was indeed attracting the malignant *sluagh*, or wind of voices, that apparently dictated verses to him.

*

The earliest emotion of worship
singed on this, my sea of thirst.
I am not equipped: genus of water,
genus of salt, to climb the tree,
the spreit-bower submersed:
cannot yet be committed to paint
nor carved, nor versed; so kneel here still,
with my tongue in my hand,
and pant.

*

The spit in my eye has not yet dispersed:
in its phlegm lens found lifeless,
I was crouched in my boat, snouted in sleep:
an eradication of dream blew into storm:
static, yet quivering, on the horizon of kelp.

*

My tongue, still blistering,
is a cracked curse between dumbness and speech;
the sand flood, my mouth,
the binder, my mouth,
work grows in its tomb
like a blight:

I have seen my statue, bitten out,

as the fisher-coals glow
in extinguishment.

*

Marginal, I cope,
time, my ageing catapult,
I restore with stones: planets of hope.

My corpse swallows one:
stern, glass eye of the throat.

Stern eye of the figurehead:
of the marine beast residing there,
colour-flooded with fear.

*

Washed up here is monochrome:
it is not season, it is not burnish,
it is neutered in colour-hope.
I have stirred its bewilderment,
tang of titanium, tang of lamp.

*

Colour escapes hue –
unilluminate bleeding –
and its bandages, the beach, stained
by the ceaseless, pressing, colourless sea
are stained by time, not temperament,
not reflection, not spectrum.

*

I acquire the taste of monochrome reason,
sit on salt licks to lick and weep
perch and insoak plenitude spreits:
seethed in and out
on blenched colourways of sleep.

*

It is perishment, says colour,
enmeshed in a vision of sight
whose reflex of fire is air,
whose beach, rolled up tight
as a parable shore, is a demon
beached in circumstance of light.

The Green and the Blue

Gerry Cambridge

for Naush Sabah

I.

Gusts off the Firth in the glassy light of a January dawn
on the morning of the bins
topple them into the street with a clatter
of cans and plastics as the wind swirls
round house-ends; who'll pick it up? Who will care?
8 a.m. No one's here. Why is that wide
front window boarded? What's the story
of what looks like the gouges of an axe
all down that white front door?
                                        Who lives here?
I do, for one. A first floor flat in this
enigmatic street that I look down onto
for signs and signals, simple enough
where a green or a blue announce an allegiance
and a Christian name marks out your tribe
so keep it safe and indeterminate
as to what your pronouns are or would be if
you cared. No pronouns given here
where the frost on January mornings
glitters on blades in the dull first light
over long-tussocked gardens in the still, locked pallor
before the rise of dawn, miles-wide, ignites
over my head on the bedroom wall to wild
orange of the local star: stellar ferocity tamed
by ninety-three million miles.
                                        Who lives here?

I study the comings and goings for clues
in these lockdown months, disinclined
to draw even a glance to my white door facing
onto the street and my upper rooms with their books and papers,
their vintage nibs of Pelikans, Swans and Blackbirds,
my old fought-for pretensions, quaint and barely
belonging, where the opposite neighbour
with his curtains always drawn
risks no crack of light to a nod or glance
of recognition, as if I didn't exist.
I flourish fine in that, it being my natural state:
head down and drawing no fire
for the blade or machete or paranoid scowl,
careful even when I take sorted items
past the downstairs flat to the bins
out back, mainly in winter darkness, covertly as if
committing some misdemeanour, as if
being human itself were a crime. Orion
perfect, enormous, glinting
high in the south over silhouetted roofs and my back plot,
the frost-glued plastic lids of the bins when lifted
crackling like minor gunshot,
and the Co-op carriers tumbling out plastic and paper, me
gazing around at the covert lives behind lit curtains,
wanting no 'x' on my bald head. I can switch to speech
learned through fifty years: *Aye. Fuckin tossers. Ya think?*
Aye, right. No way man. Surely no?
Bloody stappit tae the gunnels. Whit a fuckin moger. I joke that I keep
the picture of me shaking hands with the smiling Queen

at Buckingham Palace easy to find on my phone
among the hundreds of sky and sea. Me,
always a black crow among black crows, disguising my
                                                    white feathers.

II.

Harsh energies come to visit, right into my life,
of the pterodactyl gulls I see every day down the harbour,
necks stretched out in maniacal yelpings in mid-air, or beaks
angled down at webbed feet, then
cacklingly thrown back skywards
in attitudes of triumphal exultation:
this is me ya fuckin bampots! Mon an try yer luck! –
come to visit when the neighbour moves in downstairs: shouts
up through the floorboards
one night in late January, the old unease
of the unknown future. I take bags out to the bins
on reconnaissance in glittery dark
past the car in the drive, climb over my broken gate propped up
to keep out the dogs, and immediately
him and a pal appear at his door in the dark
talking animatedly, smoking. *Awright?*
– *Aye.*
        – *Is the caur in yer road?*
– *Na, it's fine. Movin in?* I ask.
– *Aye. Bit by bit. The last guy'd a dug,
humongous fucker. Dug hairs aw*

ower the cairpets. Ahve spent
three hunnerd quid tae clean it. An's still no clean.
You upstairs?
        — *Aye. Just since December.*
— *Ye'll hae nae boather wi me,* he says. *Ahm quiet.*
— *That's good.*
          — *Cept when there's fitbaw.* (Laughter.)
We meet chary as dogs in the night
sniffing out loyalties. In a sudden stupid spirit
of neighbourly cohesion, I say: *I'm Gerry.*
— *Dan.*
       — *Good to meet you.* I leave them
smoking and chattering in the still dark and the streetlight amber.

      *

11 a.m. the next day: the deliberately loud
blast of Rangers anthems thumping up
through the bedroom floor, a statement:
the starting trombone's jocund whoop and flourish,
Rangers, Rangers, all across the world…
Coincidence, or causality? Foreboding has me
googling, at sixty, white noise apps and sleep headbands,
ear protectors, Bluetooth noise-cancelling
Panasonic headphones. The five letters of my Christian name
a door to a world of tribal allegiances I had forgotten
through a quarter of a century away from this coast
of stark exhilarant energies, the storms rattling
in, out of the west off the Firth over Arran,

the daffodil light in a strengthening flood,
the rays spoking down from a travelling cloud
drifting like a massive galleon and the sun
a dazzleshout up in the lit high blue
and the other stars out beyond it to forever,
the billions hidden there in the roar of light.

*

A few days later, an all-night party in the flat below,
8 p.m. to 11 a.m., the doors
slamming, the *thump thump thump*
of techno, the voices raised in anger
or rank lockdown frustration. I experiment: 'brown noise'
and 'falling rain', a 'running stream', a wall of sound
I shelter behind or try to, drift unsettled, the sleep
headband tight around my brows,
wake haggard and weary at seven
in February dark with all still going below,
imagining scenarios over bottles and ring-pulls –
aye, a fuckin Pape upstairs. Fuck sake.
Wance a Pape, ayeways a Pape.
Thirty years back, a mild dispute with an Ayrshire poet,
a stalemate point I would not concede:
you fuckin Papes are ayewis the same.

*

On the Sunday that Rangers secure the League
a gang downstairs – whoops and explosive roars at a goal, and someone
banging and banging the wall so hard
the building shakes; then outside
hammering below out of sight
on the bins below my window, setting off flares
in the street, whoever they are, in a show
half provocation, half a peculiar fear
that they are nothing. Otherwise
the whole street silent. No one would want to meet
that cokehead force hyped up on Buckfast.
I write in a letter to a Muslim friend
in real time this disturbance
and my history of Catholic and Protestant
on this coast of assaulting storms.

And so begins a frequent pattern: blowout, silence, blowout, silence.
I begin to take an interest in his doings:
the early starts, the weekend blasts,
hardly condemning it. I would too,
working a digger, off to Aberdeen at 3 a.m. on a Monday
February morning in gusting chill, remembering
my hodden-doun history in this grinding county,
dozens of empties of Newcastle Brown under the step
of a damp caravan, the human cost, a sag-coated man,
of witnessing the changing lights and tremendous weathers:
between autumn showers rattling on the roof,
a cloud in the blue – over stripped, dripping woods – as white
as the page for each scribbled, small hommage
or as the backs of the whoopers down at Warwickdale's floodpools.

Inadvertently now these many years later
I have returned in the mirk of winter, quite up in the air,
trying to guess some pattern below. I become
au fait with football fixtures, Old Firm dates,
half with resentment, half
in a spirit of anthropological scrutiny,
wry at having this needling my brain,
wanting to write of birds and clouds, part-reassured
by audioblock gadgetry that means I can sleep, by powerful
ear protectors. When they are not needed
I understand perfectly *Silence is golden*;
GOLDEN; turning it over in my hands like a glowing ingot,
while immense incandescent-edged cumuli float
across the frame of my upstairs window
on days when the showers drag their veils
across the south in a slow ballet with the lit silver clouds
on horizons beyond them for miles, over new grass charged
the freshest green.

                        *

I bump into him at our doors at times. An uncertain
broken-toothed smile. Skinny as a whippet, late twenties,
cropped head, the shock-white trainers
clean as a gannet's wing over the Firth when the great bird turns in the light
and spears down like a bolt exploding
into the mackerel's world. The skinny-calved strut
in knee-length shorts in the April sun away up the street –
so much apparent in the style of walk –

with the half-drunk bottle of *Corona*,
relaxed in the Protestant culture,
the Orange social club at the end of the road.
It is all belonging and desire for "home",
the same ease that I have with my Irish cousins
though I've made my own place in lines of verse.
Encountering him at the door one day,
as an aside, as if it were nothing, a mere afterthought,
I broach the subject of the music's volume.
Ah didnae ken. Next time it's too loud
jist come doon an chap on the door. I understand
this puts the onus back on me by apparent sleight of hand –
Unconscious, or sleekit ruse? A Sunday night
of thumping music, I take bags to the bins
in the dark past his door peculiarly open –
glimpse the changing disco lights of the music system
like a dim-lit club's in the living room,
bleak world without women,
and no one there. I knock on the door:
he appears from a room at the side,
all high-fives and coked bonhomie at 11 p.m.:
– *Music too loud? We takin the piss?*
Takin the cunt eh?
                              – *Aye, a bit loud.*
– *Mon in man! Fancy a line an a can? A wee dance?*
He mimics Travolta to 'Night Fever'.
I politely decline this disarming notion, seeing
how all too easily it could break out in choruses
of being *knee-deep in Fenian blood,*

but intrigued at the thought
of being undercover, compelled to join in.
Does he know I'm a Pape, or was? I haven't a clue.
Upstairs again, the music is suddenly decibels louder
but stops at midnight and whoever is down there
drifts among dreams in a blessèd calm.

III.

Past the sour reek of hash, away from the
lines of shops, down the harbourside, wild
reptilian gulls rifle the bins and scatter
the takeout boxes, the plastic cartons, pecking the foil
off the tiny containers of sauces, or swooping
on the drake red-breasted mergansers resplendent
in glossy moss green and reds with Mohican crests
when each bobs up with a small shore crab
and tries to gulp it down before the gulls pile in;
diving again to resurface elsewhere and hurriedly
angling the ten spiked legs for a tossed-back gape
in advance of the blizzarding scavengers. And up and down
the salt estuary through spring and summer
go the Sandwich terns, white and black-crowned, crested elegance,
languorous dipping flight and blade screech cries,
plunging for sand eels: a little splash, the shiver-shake
of the salt drops off when they rise again,
the small, dark fish hung from the blade-beak, daemonic energy
dawn to dusk. Gone
far over the curve of the sea in autumn. Irvine to Ghana.

The migrants pass through in September.
One dusk on the empty beach, where I find on a metal pole
a mile along the commercially printed sticker, *All Taigs are Targets*,
in the roar and spume of the tideline, six
sanderlings, nonstop specks on the shore. Where have they come from?
Where are they going? On the cardiograph of foam and flotsam
and tidal bits on the wet-gleamed sand up ahead in failing light,
I bring them close through the Opticrons,
the diminutive waders, all silvergray and white,
black-legged and beaked, darting, pecking,
sprinting up the hissing sand from the froth of a breaking wave,
mad to feed before the dark descends.
They accelerate before me on the beach ahead as I walk back. So
I detour out and away from the tideline,
try to overtake them and leave them to peace,
which they don't understand of course and keep
trying to outrun me with quick little head-up sprints,
as if in a race with each other, or a five-a-side game,
the black legs blurring like a watch's cogs, till I finally manage
to outdistance the six, each of them perfect
and each from each indistinguishable
as if fresh-minted from the hand of God. How can such vulnerable,
uncossetted creatures look so pristine in the roar of the wind?
Wanting nothing from anyone, owning nothing but their small frames.
Darkness is coming, little ones! Feed! Among the crash of the waves,
gifted with the gleam of wildness, I carry on into our own filthed future,
leave them behind undisturbed, little masterpieces of barbule and beak
to be gone by tomorrow to wherever they go.

Brexshitland

Alberto Fernández Carbajal

Even in the plain-speaking North
you are cushioned by English politeness
Everyone likes the fact you're
Spanish
They have houses in Fuengirola or Frigiliana
They love the sound of your name
try to roll their r's without falling on their
arse
But behind all the diplomacy lurks the truth
many of these people voted
Leave
because of a rancid version of nationalism or
because of an algorithm courtesy of Cambridge Anilitica
that made them distance themselves from everything
that brought you here and made you the person you are
This is my home but not my country becomes your mantra
The only places that feel remotely yours
are the hills and the valleys that are older than
Great Britain
older even than the English
Churn Milk Joan doesn't know she once used
to divide the land
She's now a stone who's lost her marbles
(no longer a boundary but an image in a Ted Hughes poem)
The Calder knows
The oaks know
The grouse don't know what country they
shit on, whether they are free from Europe or not
They spread their wings and flee
while humans shoot themselves in the foot

Clapped Out Anglia

Jimmy Andrex

And its toes hurt from being too big for its boots
and its feet were anchored like a dead tree's roots
and its soles were covered in guilty scars
and its boots were made for walking though these days it goes by car
till it piled on weight through lack of labour
and its knees ached like a retired footballer

fuming in a queue trying to get away to the seaside.

And its belly was full of fattening treats
and its dreams were influenced by late-night cheese
and its spine was a motorway started by slaves
and its limbic system was sketched on the walls of caves
and its neck was cricked from looking back
and its memory was like my senile mother's – well, you have to laugh

fuming in a queue trying to get away to the seaside.

And its heart was an object of bitter arguments
and its heart was located by inaccurate measurements
and its heart was broken by inevitable penalties
and its heart beat faster when looking out to sea
and its heart beat stronger when all people got the vote
and its heart was left in a seafront disco

fuming in a queue trying to get away to the seaside.

And its fingers smelled of many pies
and its dying jokes were rescued by Morecambe and Wise
and its suit was tailored but didn't half niff
and its hair was like an old Ted's quiff
and its conscience was apt to nip out for a fag
as its hands rummaged in its pocket for a flag

fuming in a queue trying to get away to the seaside.

And its eyes were bigger than its belly
and its teeth were chalk cliffs chattering into jelly
and its accent changed as the weather got more chilly
and its mouth spoke Norse translations of Stormzy
and its eyes looked outwards but pretended not to
like a teenage lad outside a girls' school

fuming in a queue trying to get away to the seaside.

Bridges are restless places, neither here nor there *
Anne Caldwell

There's a slatted bridge over a burn, deep in the Galloway Forest. Pine trees hold the banks together and the air is resin thick. This is the kind of bridge where a car might stop and a man climb out, check for passing traffic and click open the boot. But not today. A woman in a Skoda has spent hours on the winter motorway. She pauses for a break and twists open a flask of black coffee. The bridge creaks a little, like a knee joint, flexing. She's driving to see her lover. Will she still recognise his smell? What on earth will they say to each other after all those daily texts about politics, the morning weather, rapid flow testing and their virtual lives? There are trolls beneath the arches of her mind. She can hear them smirking. *He won't like that roll of Christmas fat around your belly. He won't want to spend hours with this dumb creature you've become.* So much water under the bridge. She's a woman who's misplaced herself, whose body quivers with elvers. Should she turn back? Her house is so silent you can hear field mice in the attic.

* Rosie Garland

Scottish Tenner

Ben Banyard

It's strange to have cash these days.
The notes crackle in my wallet,
poke above receipts and loyalty cards.

One of them is a Clydesdale tenner –
legal tender south of the border, never you mind –
but I see doubt flicker across the assistant's face.

She eyes Robbie Burns with suspicion,
flips it over to the view of Edinburgh
as though looking for instructions.
I dare her: *Is there a problem?*
She glances back at me, shakes her head,
presses a few buttons on the till and gets my change.

I see my note has a little compartment
all to itself. *Have a nice day*, she smiles.

Afternoon in a Northern Town

Atar Hadari

Waking up at two in a pale front room
in an English northern town.
The light a beach swept clean by storm,
the windows high as cliff edge stones

and realising this is where it ends,
these curtains, sunlight over the bay,
a shudder in the middle of twilight,
stars winking before they begin to disappear.

The Only Way to Lose an Accent

Natalie Holborow

Behind the door, I hang my tongue
on a coat peg, this silence a way to lose
an accent. A sob is language dismantled.
There's a pause that follows, a room
that smells of *hiraeth*, a turmoil of coal and copper.

How startling to learn how much world
the mind can yearn for, the deep *tonnau*
of sheer blue, how the moon strikes borders to ice.
The boot marks of Britain press landslides
into coastlines, plough the bones of our valleys,
their frail sails bearing the hopeless
into the fray of its stubborn anthem.

It's Not Ideal but It Is What It Is

Betsie Flynn

my real accent crawls in when I'm tired
or drunk
the one I've stumbled over stiles to avoid
the one smoothed like river glass
after years of watching corseted side-burned period dramas
BBC women with their clipped tones
nodding along to gardening shows with Mum
as if I would ever learn to chart the course of seasons across my beds
that not-quite London drag and silence
of the East Kent where Nigel Farage thought to gain footing
at least it wasn't quite as strangled as I'd feared
at least he didn't bound into Thanet
lop-eared and looking for a smile
getting one and taking heart
it was closer than I'd like though
closer than bedding down with crabs
that hackle and scurry across lugwormed sand
moist and desperate for silence

Taxi Driver

Safia Khan

I am relieved to see a tasbeeh
hanging behind the air freshener.
After exchanging niceties and village names,
he tells me the story he cannot forget:

> At school there was a girl who dated a gora,
> and of course we knew,
> but nobody said anything,
> in case the girl's brothers found out,
> because in those days, they'd kill him on sight.
> Anyway, she was his girlfriend,
> and one day I heard him in the playground,
> talking to his mates about her,
> you know, how boys do, and he says to his mates
> that he's seeing a Paki. Later that day
> he went to kiss her behind the bins,
> and after, winked at his mates.

He glances at me through the rear-view mirror

> Do you understand, Puttar?
> It doesn't matter whether you
> drive their cabs or cure their cancer.
> There is no we. Only us. And them.

The Dreaming

Bob Beagrie

The people are plummeting from the edge of the cliffs:
men, women, children. Many have closed their eyes
to the drop, to the waves below manhandling rocks,
but one young fellow holds tight to the peak of his cap
while yelling, 'I'm gonna ride my very own unicorn!'
You've got to give his commitment credit, another
bloke's saluting the sky, bellowing Rule Britannia,
a girl flaps her arms, willing sudden metamorphosis
into a kittiwake, some are yanking off clothes mid-fall
streamlining themselves to herring, plaice or sand eels,
fingers clawing at their necks to quickly fashion gills.
Some are waving, resolutely, in their backward descent
at our snowflake hesitation at the land's crumbling lip,
watching ropes they've tied around our stalks uncoil.
We too shall become fish, bird, seal, crab and horsefly;
first, like the firm believers we inadvertently follow, we
must let go of our familiar lives and embrace this fall.

Pathogen

Bob Beagrie

"Thy subjects' blood
With fire and sword
Cries vengeance Lord."
Parliamentarian motto from
'The Great Eclipse of the Sun', 1644

"Hate begets hate;
violence begets violence;
toughness begets a greater toughness."
Dr Martin Luther King, 1958

like someone forgot to turn the key, shoot the bolt,
guard the cage door and now its loose, running wild,
raging on pent-up retribution for its incarceration;
not hiding in the undergrowth, a hole in the ground
but behind a look, beneath a word, within a promise,
travelling in a crowd, forming clusters along chains
of transmission, hitchhiking on breath and bodily fluids,
a stowaway in an attitude, an illegal immigrant riding
the virulent fear of itself gone viral, breaking-out
with a swelling of symptoms: the sharpened accusations
of 'susceptibles', slammed doors, raised voices, dog shit
through the letter box, broken windows, burning homes,
a contagion of tears, smoking guns, targeted spot-checks,
round-ups, stretched necks, tightening nooses; spreading
its invisible infection from host to vulnerable host
through mounted charges, routs, panicked retreats,
infiltrating the blood, penetrating the lymph node,
concealed there, trafficking pathways of incubation

through dendritic and monocyte cells; the brain's
blockades breached, the heart besieged, kinship ties
in tatters, trust a looted keepsake; corrupting all it
touches, draining its juices, carts piled with cadavers –
Bring out your dead!
Bring out your dead!
Bring out your dead!

This Realm, This England

Rory Waterman

He sparks the flint – his face and hand flare amber –
and grins. The isled flame judders in freezing air.
He dabs it gently to the moistened jamb.
'Shhhh!' it sighs, and takes. We leave it there

and when we come past later in the morning
the rafters are charred stumps, the walls are bare,
and neighbours gather, pointing, by police tape,
and we nudge to it, as close as we dare.

And by us, nested halfway up a fir,
blinking, turning, and though we're not aware
of it yet, a camera in a dome
reflects our will, then watches us walk home.

Brexit Explained

Cathy Bryant

Brexit: Gove warns of referendum
if MPs don't back PM's deal.

Referendum: Brexit warns of Gove
if MPs don't deal PM's back.

PM's deal: referendum warns of Brexit
if MPs don't Gove back.

MP's PM: refer slithy Gove
gives Brexit back to deal dum-dum.

Endum AM: PM gyres Govy deal
warning breakfast backpack.

Warning: error 404 exit fear
back back back/ deal deal deal
Gove oven-ready.

Wurra wexit wove wear
wendum weel weelly
wee wee wee all the way
what the

Good Friday in the Calder Valley

Charlotte Murray

On Heptonstall's main street, boots hammer a beat
on the cobblestones under the clink of home-sewn costumes.
They ring out over the valley while church bells hang still
and muted beside Weavers Square. Faces protrude
from the windows of soot-darkened cottages.

A homage to mince pies begins and builds to a boom
echoing from stone. Some know the words by heart.
By the graveyard wall St. George leaps at Bold Slasher
with a clack of wooden swords. His roar sends crows
scattering from branches. Three kisses for a crème egg:

some women push to the front, smiles like headlights,
others duck behind cagouled backs. Baskets empty
of still-warm buns, branded with floury crosses.
A torrent of coins waterfalls into plastic buckets.
Some years icicles drape from Plath's headstone, today

bluebells lean out, listening. Beer flows from plastic steins
like the river through the vale and footsteps become
unsteady stones to walk across. Words are forgotten
and invented, swords clash and clash again, watched by
a translucent moon peering over the rolling cloud bank.

Outside The Cross, a hog roast spits, where the Coiners
once silenced a man with fire. On the muddied track
to Hardcastle Crags, dusk gathers behind walls, beneath trees,
their leaves trembling under the wind's bluster.
A bag is slipped from a cold fist to a sweaty palm.

Bagpipe Music 2022

Dave Wakely

Let's all hold hands and pretend it's all halcyon
and nothing's gone rotten in darling old Albion.
How could it be when we've such a fine champion
burying his nose in the trough?

Look how we sail with this hand on the rudder,
this dickhead whose judgements could never be dudder.
No matter how fiercely we tremble or shudder
there's just too much piss to shake off.

He's putting the villain in Villanelle,
warping and wefting a cod Latin spell,
while he's twinning the Garden of Eden with Hell
and then skipping off for a shag.

He governs in gestures and grand gusts of words
as clotted and curdled as yesterday's curds,
selling false hope while we paddle in turds
and offering a towel made of flags.

Now normality's gone to meet its maker,
shall we welcome the Amish, the Puritans and Quakers
to sort wheat from chaff and heroes from fakers
While we play Angry Birds on our phones?

Let our children dig trenches to plant next year's carrots
to stuff in their ears to silence the parrots
who drown their concerns in subsidised clarets
as red as the blood in our bones.

Will good things still come if we patiently wait
or will compost and chalk be our ultimate fate?
Let's shake when we meet at Heaven's Gate
and talk about who was to blame.

Let latter day Jesus' wring hands for sinners
while Marys stay home and bring them their dinners,
pimping the privilege of society's winners.
Some things are always the same.

Political Studies

Dave Wakely

Britannia's seizures have led to amnesia,
she denies everything that she did.
Her glamour and glory's turned out cheap and whorey,
Now she'll flash you her tits for a quid.

At this speed you can tell that we're off straight to hell –
these handcarts won't handle the bends –
their engines are stoked by privileged blokes
who've auctioned their souls to their friends.

And hey diddle diddle, they're all on the fiddle
while our world goes arse over tit:
their position's secure while we stand in manure.
(If nowt grows in it, lad, call it shit).

Watch them toast their campaigns with taxpayers' champagne
while we burn our tables and chairs.
No, they don't hate the judges, just give them wee nudges,
then laugh as they fall down the stairs.

See them run country miles to avoid public trials
so frit at their possible fate.
The Beatles were wrong, Albion's favourite song
is All You Need Is Hate.

We're in with both feet, chowing down on whale meat,
pretending we're smitten with gristle.
They still tell us we're loved but when push comes to shove
what they mean is bend over and whistle.

Dog Day

Gary Allen

Monday is a dog day, especially in November
when there is no light to speak of and lines
of cars move along choked streets
like fish under the surface of murky water.
The office workers drink giant cups of Fair Deal
coffee, holding them like spiritual chalices
to a hidden sun, faces pallid with LED lights
in rooms decked out with rows of indiscriminate
chairs like a modernist church in Iceland.
The traffic lights might be on green
at the intersection to the city and the ferry terminal,
but the bus driver isn't sure, like the huddled
cardboard-covered seals beached
in the subway opposite, or the tracksuit figures
pushing prams and supermarket trolleys
Mother Courage-style to the high-rise flats,
the seagulls gliding in with the fishing fleet,
crucifix lights of the plane booming in
above sleeping hills and tower blocks,
white faces at the porthole windows
dreaming of the places they call home.
And someone has died in the Salvation Army
armchair in front of the daytime telly,
that piece of bacon they were saving
for breakfast fallen between two dishes. And you
just know that there will be no daylight today,
only a grey dampness of car horns and feet
and the suffocation of a great blanket
set over the city by a bored Thanatos.

Everydog
Jim Greenhalf

In spite of never being asked to appear
on Newsnight, The One Show or Strictly Come Dancing,
I hear that an international poetry agency
with a data base and algorithms,
is probing my background to see if I ever said anything interesting,
controversial or, God forbid, offensive, about anybody.

If fortune should ever thrust celebrity upon me
while I still have teeth, I have no interest in saying
'Wow!', 'Awesome', or 'Iconic', on national tv;
nor in exploring my antecedents with Davina McCall.
If siblings are in hiding here, there or anywhere,
keep it that way. I do not wish them well.

I do not yearn to save humanity or rescue the planet.
And I'm not on a journey. When my time is done, I hope to go
into that good night without too much whining.
We are mostly mongrels trying to escape the kennel
and avoid the fate of refugees, washed up like seaweed on Dover beach.
Not every dog has its day in the sun.

No Dogs

Michael Stewart

Dog couldn't get served in the Grain and Hop.
The barman pointed to a sign on the backbar: No Dogs.
He wanted to see the Renaissance watercolours exhibition
at the Victoria and Albert Museum.
The receptionist refused to print him a ticket,
but he ducked the rope at the entrance.
He skipped the miniatures of Anne of Cleves,
went straight to the Jacob Jordaens.
When he tried to book for Götterdämmerung,
the online system rejected his Amex card.
The sommelier at the Dorchester
said the wine was too complex for his palate.
He was kicked out of Fortnum and Mason's
by two goons in top hat and tails
even though he'd prepaid for the Fu Dai hamper.

He padded grey pavements,
doors latched, hasped, boarded, and hooked.
Then the rain came down,
lead shot fell from pewter clouds.
Dog looked for shelter.
Every bar and every public house:
no dogs no dogs no dogs.
His fur clung to his skin,
rain ran down the gutter of his nose.
He shook his coat and shivered.

He traipsed through North Parade
along the main road out of town.
He hit the fields east of the city,
the dust of his feet into the country,
dusk, frost, feet worn,
needed a roof over his head
to rest his bones.
Out on the edge of Tong Moor
a farmhouse glowed on a hill,
warm lights poured and puddled,
a sclerotic farmer slammed the door.
It was a big, fat, bald, NO.
Found a kennel by a mistal,
trudged to the mouth of its entrance:
barred, bolted, barbed, razor wired,
topped by two combi locks,
a sign above the lintel:
NO FUCKING DOGS.

Oh England, I Love You

Georgia Hilton

but I do not understand you.
You're the ageing parent
with a chronic anger problem.
The one we worry about.

Placing obstacles in your own way
then cursing the neighbours
when you trip over them,
I don't think you're okay.

You're the boomer, embracing
Zoom, but fallen into the black hole
of internet conspiracy theories.
You're doomed to relive the war

in glorious Technicolor, even though
you're too young to remember it.
You say it was your Finest Hour…
meanwhile you let the scammers in.

They put their feet up on your coffee table,
drink tea from your best porcelain,
then invite their friends over –
those flattering rogues who tell you

you can have your youth again – they
smile at you, eat your shortbread,
steal your grandkids' inheritance,
scratch the paintwork on their way out.

You think *what nice boys they are*
because they speak well, went to private schools,
remind you of a time when
everything made sense.

Medlars

Geraldine Clarkson

England like a medlar, unbletted.
When they come to score the cardboardy
hide, to get at the lush nostalgic mud
inside, the sting
causes them to backtrack
and search for better butter elsewhere.

Let the hard-to-grow fruit grow ruddy
like fat peasant cheeks
etched into blue, glass sky –
not splayed on racy dishes for royalty –
the Kingdom split, grinning wide
at the hinges, creaking, just holding for now.

Cofiwch Dryweryn

Glyn Edwards

He swears he can't remember it swollen so high,
so we balance at his wet window on tall stools
like chess pieces, calculating the river's rise
and counting down to when its banks will break. All rules
revised, we start to drum and pound upon the glass:
ten, nine, eight, seven, six, five, four, three, hysterically
we chant, daring the day to deny our trespass,
but the fields and farms we've forged into our grid city
withstand. We descend from our nests to the classroom,
stills of subdued Treweryn are on the board now:
its graveyards underwater, a church spire that is
lifting its head at low tide, families dredged from their homes
as water surges in at the speed of life. *How
are we elevated by the sinking of villages?*

Happy Breed

Gregory Woods

We islanders believe ourselves immune.
A stretch of sea will save us from the plague
of foreign influence, its currents sly
and unforgiving—not unlike ourselves.
Our character was formed before the whim

and froth of history could weaken it,
emerging from the chalk and limestone uplands
like fossils raised when continents collide
and seabeds come to rest on mountaintops.
We change for no one, no one changes us.

Processing down the enfilade of time,
we make of accident a history
befitting our approval of ourselves.
The ancient myths our ancestors contrived
a century ago, the rhyming tales

of bloodshed civilised by good intentions,
persuade us we were always who we are,
or like to think we are, allowing us
the comfort of a stiff complacency.
There's no misgiving in our DNA.

Commuters

Jack Faricy

Standing in a muddy tunnel
under Eastbound traffic
where the farmer keeps
pallets and breeze blocks
and bulk bags of logs,
I watch the pulsing rain
come in off the moors,
the pummelling wind,
the gust-whipped waves
crashing over the rim
and gushing down the spillway
in white, curved surges,
and even though it's grim
I'd rather be stuck here
than up there with them.

Keep Out the Poets

Jennifer Johnson

There's too many here already.
They frighten me because
of how they stick together.
They don't even try to act normal.
They use words I can't understand
just to put me down.
If you go to where they live
it's disgusting, full of dusty books.
You can't breathe for all the dust!
That's another reason I don't like them.
They've got time to read
but, of course, most of them
don't do a proper job like me.
Once there was this woman
at the place where I worked.
She seemed OK but I found out
she was a poet.
That's how they're taking over,
changing our culture.
You hear their arty stuff
at weddings and funerals
like how we talk's no good.
My daughter has to read poems
at school. They're so miserable.
What we need is cheering up.
You'd think with their education
they'd make themselves look smart
but they go round looking like students.
That's why I don't want any more
living where I do.

Passages

Jennifer Johnson

In this coastal town
poverty protects itself
with flags and dogs.
Visitors climb to the fort
that guarded against strangers
for millennia, look down
on ferries that feed this port.

Underneath the castle
lies chalk of the sort
teachers taught and
frightened me with,
rock worm-eaten
by defensive passages
carved out in countless wars.

These chalk tunnels
dig into my memory,
my childhood obscured
by Sudanese sandstorms.
A plane simply flew my family
into clearer weather,
first to Malta, then London.

Are those head-scarfed women
sitting on the bench
tourists or have they made
one of those epic journeys
you see on the news,
crossing shifting sand dunes,
Mediterranean waves?

The women put on dark coats,
cover their bright clothes.

Together

Joe Allen

A mass of dead crows
tied together with string
along the roadside

like a van load
of workmen
picked out from their mates –

we become hardened
to suffering
just news

like earth-cracks
like tsunamis

like a politician
dancing in the aisle
of a supermarket

with a Kingsmill loaf
on his head.

A' Fàgail Bhreatainn

Pàdraig MacAoidh

Tha sinn air a bhith a' fàgail an eilein-sa,
a ghràidh, fad ar beathan, am bàta a' siubhal
a-mach à Lochbraon, na peileagan mar dhìochuimhne
a' sgeadachadh uisge na stiùire.

Chan e aithreachas a bh' ann a stiùir
sinn on charraig sin, creagach le dùr-bheachd
càrn-chogaidh, na h-aon fhreagairtean simplidh
a' leantainn na h-aon cheistean fhaoin

agus ged 's e aisling a th'ann – solais fhaoin
a' taomadh tro shlatan fiodha – cha tèid
a cho-lìonadh am measg cuìltean falbh
sgìrean ionmhais, na calmain a' piocadh air a' ghlainne.

Tha gach facal a-nis cho trid-shoilleir ri ghlainne
ach chan eil sin ag ràdh g' eil iad fìor,
a ghràidh, agus chan eil tagsaidh ri fhaighinn
airson gaoil neo sgillin, sgeulachd ruadh no òran ùr:

fad ar beathan a' feitheamh air oirthir ùr,
crùbagan nam falach anns a' bhàrr-roc fhuar;
a dh'aindeoin reothairt 's conntraigh 's ar seachd
leisgeulan, cha till sinn chaoidh dhan eilean-sa.

Leaving Britain

Peter Mackay

We have been leaving this island,
my love, all our lives, the boat tacking
out of Loch Broom, the porpoise
like forgetfulness gilding our wake.

We have no regrets propelling us
from that rock, the stony insistence
of its war memorials, the same simple answers
to the same vapid questions

and though this is just a dream – a washy light
pouring through wooden slats – it will never
come to life in the empty nooks
of business districts, pigeons pecking at the glass.

Each word is now see-through as thin glass
but that doesn't mean they are true,
my love, and there are no taxis to be got
for love or pennies, red tales or re-sung songs:

all our lives waiting on new frontiers,
crabs skulking in cold seaweed;
despite the ebb and flow of our sevenfold
excuses, there's no returning to this island.

It

John Newsham

It starts with a trigger warning, straight out of the birth canal: *What lies ahead may cause upset.* It logs on to Twitter and prefers not to use Its own name. It takes a shit on the Union Jack. It wipes its arse with the EU stars. It takes the Tory politician and sticks him in a council flat he can't afford to heat. It tells him to budget. It takes the Labour politician and sticks her in the council flat next door. The one with the nice red curtains and fuck-all inside. It can't remember the name of a single Lib Dem. It rounds up all the centrists and the BBC reporters with public-school accents and supply-teacher smiles. It drops them into a cell with an Overton Window and no door. It drags everyone out of the House of Lords and tells them to fuck off. It taps the Brexiteer on the shoulder. It tells him he's thick as shit. It taps the Remainer on the shoulder. It enquires: *Why do you think you lost? Could you not articulate the arguments that would have demonstrated your superior intellect?* It walks away, whistling. It screams select lines from Siegfried Sassoon through the two minutes' silence. It covers itself in poppies and departs from the cenotaph in a nuclear submarine. It takes the culture warriors. The woke and the anti-woke. The PC mob and the anti-PC mob. It invents problems for them to ponder like a Zen master: *Did you know if you speak English during Ramadan you get arrested and sent to a jail where all the food is halal?* It takes the cisgender man and the TERF and the white woman and the woman of colour and the man of colour and the lesbian of colour and the homosexual of no colour and it pretends to be confused. It gives the men's rights activist a slap on the arse and tells the feminist to man up. It takes the binary and the non-binary and the bisexual and the bi-curious and says: *By-the-time-we've-labelled-us-all-we'll-set-the-whole-world-right.* They look nonplussed. It grins. It takes the Muslim and the Christian and the Jew. It leads them through the checkpoint past the armed Israeli guards. It takes them to the tomb of Abraham and asks them what would happen if we pulled him out. It makes them hold hands in a circle and pray. It leaves to use the toilet. It reads the atheist a poem and asks him to underline the metaphors. It pats him on the head. It woos the agnostic and sits and holds her hand. It potters off. It takes all of the fascists and It marches them to Auschwitz. It bolts those awful doors and turns on the gas. It hears them gasp. It rounds up all the communists at gunpoint in the middle of the night. It locks them in the gulag. It makes them debate class theory and human ideals while they starve and scheme against each other. It lines them up against the wall. It takes me then It takes you. It takes everybody else. All of us who know we've seen the light. It leads us to the darkness. To that place where every one of us is wrong. It ends. It ends with a trigger warning, right there with the final gasp: *What lies ahead may cause upset.*

Launderette With Single Figure #1

Kerry Featherstone

The launderette backdrop is unbending
as you stand
from a plastic chair, complaining.

Washers waist-high,
leaving your chest
outlined against the cracked
window. Heaving weight towards
the dryers as powder slides on
nylon, melamine, plastic flooring.

Lifting
a black sack of wet kit
to the mouth of the machine,
you grunt again. A quid for seven minutes.
The dryers turn anti-clockwise.
The heat rises.

Greys marble
the face of the dryer. You pull down
a sweated sleeve that reads *Help for Heroes*
over an elbow hatched with eczema.

Mist cools on the chair legs, condensation
rolls over the damp powder counter, sticking
claggy lumps to your bag.

The time is nearly
up: retrieve the clothes. They'll cool
on the way back to the flat, and cling
to your arms as you drape them
on broken chair backs.

Now your shape blacks the space
Between my seat and the clean
light that flies through the door
as you push open, drag
the holdall, hitch it to your shoulder
and grind
towards the bus stop.

Commissioners of Sewers

Steve Ely

This poem describes how the Crown, aided and abetted by sundry Lords, courtiers and adventurers, used prerogative power and the state's monopoly of violence to drain and enclose the fenland commons, extort, expropriate & expel the commoners, and auction off the Commonwealth to privy investors. The Commissioners of Sewers would conspire with landowners and adventurers to declare a given tract of fenland 'hurtfully surrounded', contrary to efficiency and the national good. The Commissioners would then lay a tax on the relevant parishes to cover the costs of the drainage, whether the parishioners wanted the land drained or not. They invariably did not, because their livelihoods were dependent on their commoners' rights to exploit the fenland's bounty, and in paying for its drainage they'd be funding their own ruin. After the commoners refused or failed to pay the tax, the Commissioners would then impose the works, which were undertaken by the landowners and adventurers, often with the active support of the king. Enclosure would follow, with the commoners' rights being unilaterally withdrawn, and the plots sold off to Dutch and Huguenot settlers, whose loyalty – to their landlords, the drainage and the Protestant Crown – might be assured. The commoners' protests were put down with the full force of the state: militia and vigilante groups were loosed on the Enemy Within; dissidents were murdered, assaulted, imprisoned; 'ringleaders' were brought before the Star Chamber and subjected to astronomical, unpayable fines – equivalent to millions in current exchange value – resulting in committal to the Fleet for non-payment of tax and fine; unless, of course, they signed affidavits renouncing their rights and consenting to the drainage, at which point, tax and fine would be waived and the fettered might be released – to labour on the settlers' farms, or to leave their lands forever. Thus the 'Drainage of the Fens', generally characterised as a glorious feat of 'British' engineering that transformed unproductive, uninhabited and pestilential waste into habitable, rich and fertile farmland, able to feed the growing population of a go-getting nation on the rise – that is, as the perfect form of nationalist, capitalist, 'we're-all-in-it-together' progress – was in fact a ruthless act of imperial violence, ethnic cleansing and colonial plantation, no different in kind to similar English or British atrocities in the Americas, Australasia, Africa, Ireland and Scotland. See also *Enclosure Movement, the.* The Scotch king, Man of Blood and pleonexic grasper cHARLES sTEWART was the primary instigator of this action against his subjects, but the following stuffed their faces at the trough: Francis Russell: percentage man, fence-sitter, Earl of Bedford; Saint Corny Vermuyden: gambler, undertaker, Ponzi fraudster; Sir Miles Sandys: parvenu, ring-sniffer, addled Parliament-arian; Sir Thomas Lovell: lumper, scrumper, Pode Hole pumper; Sir Philibert Vernatti: a Dutchman, Gentleman of the King's Bedchamber; Sir Jacob Cats: double-Dutch, knighted by the King on account of coin, adventurer and poet, 'more renowned than read'; Sir Robert Heath: pro-forma used-car ducker-and-diver – Archer, Farage, Johnson; Sir Edward Heron: delinquent, gangster, bent copper; Sir Anthony Thomas: swindler, debtor, man of mean estate;

Robert Killigrew: privy-this, I-dub-thee-that, farmer of corners and guaranteed profit; and his son, Sir William: vast gainer, Member of Parliament, *poet* – dissociation of sensibility in the dried peats of the coffy house, the emergence of the Poetry Voice in the Restoration Court – elocute murderers, slavers and scammers, up for the Forward Prize. The poem is over. There will be a test.

The Commissioners of Sewers were bodies appointed from the ranks of the nobility, landowners and relevant State representatives to oversee the drainage of the fens in the 17th century. They played a major – and often legally questionable and deeply corrupt – role in the process.

Island

Kevin Higgins

after Wislawa Szymborska

Where men with shiny scalps
fight for the right to dye
hair they no longer have
any colour they want.

Here, garbage can by magicked
into its opposite by the mere act
of attaching to it the word: Great.

Proud nation that pays
redundant assembly line operatives
to sell photoshopped versions of itself
to tourists from its former colonies.

Raised voices in its cathedral city tea rooms.
So shrill a cup gets chipped
in the course of the argument
and a scone is left behind on the plate.

The roses around its cottage gates try to forget.
But, elsewhere, the dead factory remembers.

And the disgraced estate agent tries to secure the door
on what was once British Home Stores
but can't fathom the lock.

Welcome to the Neighbourhood

Mark Connors

Hi. Just thought I'd pop over
to invite you to ours.
We're having people over Friday.
You in? Brilliant!
How's the unpacking going?
Have you met your neighbours yet?
Trish at Number 7's great.
She runs a salon,
Hair Flick, next to the deli.
If you decide to colour your hair,
don't look any further.
The woman by the pub
made me look like Keith Lemon.
Do you talk shop?
I know what you teachers are like.
If so, I'll stick you on the end
with Sam and Alice from the high school.
She's due in late February.
And then there's Tommy.
He's tastier than a free-range egg
and he's got a right yolk on him.
Lovely man. Divorced. Just saying.
Sporty type. Likes to run and hike.
I wouldn't kick him out of the King Size.
Then there's Marcus and Sally.
They own loads of property
and do lots of work for charity.
I'm doing Tapas. You'll love it.
No one sees colour on our street.

Goole voted Leave

Nick Allen

waking in the alley behind Jefferson Street
   the sky has lines of perspective
drawing the gaze to unexpected places like a painting
   by Burdall or a Mondrian

reappraisal of space   wires spoke from the
   telegraph pole cutting sky
into pie-slice portions   a chart that wants to represent
   something I lack

the tools to grasp   perhaps the number of syringes found
   on the footbridge
over the tracks on each day of the week since January
   perhaps children

going to school without a warm meal
   or the number of people who have
had their benefits cut because they are deemed *fit to work*
   black and green

bruises line the street that cant find the right track
   sheets pinned as make-do curtains
across peeling frames and a satellite dish rusting
   on the wall of each house

capturing nothing worthwhile from the ether
    these tight terraces once
filled with dock workers   railwaymen and landlocked sailors
    the people

whose industry filled Lowthers murals   now town walls hum
    with mis-spelling
and mis-appropriation comparing Brexiteers with *Suffagettes*
    no more

Blood Alley just a street with a Wetherspoons
    a Greggs making *hot dinners*
for everyone   and the *youngest junkie in Britain*
    according to the local rag

Crowds Will Gather on the Beach

Penny Blackburn

The signal for your life to fall apart
will be the smallest flicker of dread.
As easy to miss as a trickle of smoke
beneath the arcade's kaleidoscopic lights, its jangling
rings and buzz, the clattering penny cascade
and rattling shoot-em-ups.

Within an hour, the flames will caress everything.
Fire crews will press hovercrafts
into service, but from the moment
the call comes in, they know
that nothing they can do will be sufficient.

Your pavilion will buckle. Glass fracture.
Paint return to liquid. Your deck will fall, planks
sycamore-winging their way into the dark space below.
News footage will show the black-grey-black sheet of smoke
that chokes the shadows
watching, curious, from the sand.

Dawn. You will be smouldering,
ribbed ironwork still too hot
for the gulls and starlings that wish to settle.
Stripped to your silhouette struts
– ashy-layered over rust – you will wait
for the tide to wash around you.

You will plead with the sea to leave you what is left.

The crowds will disperse; like the seabirds
they have their own lives to be flying along with.

Bog & Fen

Robin Gurney

When you tell me you are 'English to the core'
    I think of old wetland trees
whose insides rot away and leave their trunk a hollow ribcage.

I see you grasping for your
        strong   *pure*   heartwood
    and finding only mess, decay,
that which time has transformed beyond understanding.

There is no 'pure' in 'Anglo-Saxon' – the very term is hybrid.

Millennia of inward-moving tracks
        have left this body politic lattice-worked with scars:
Angles, Saxons, Jutes, Britons, Danes, Romans, Normans –
all were swallowed by the land   in bones and blood,
their boundaries blurring further   each time we till the earth.

You and I are not 'indigenous'   for being white and born here.
there is no 'unspoilt' heritage to claim – we're mongrels,
    bred by brutal tides.

This isle of mist and rain and shivers   was colonised so many times
our oldest gods were lost to memory,   our metals drained for Rome.
Then we turned tyrant,   spread across the world like creeping damp
to fill that hollow-hearted tree   with stolen gold –
with bodies, stories, everything that caught our eyes:
as if theft could replace long-missing things.
Once invaded, then invaders.   We are   *not*   *victims*   *now,*

and when you talk of 'invasions' taking place today,
    tidal waves of immigration –
No.   Learn.   Our.   History.   These 'waves' are ripples
    from the storms we caused,
washing up the drowning and displaced on this hostile shore –
    and you treat them with hate,
as if our ancestors didn't cross the sea to come here too?
        As if our ancestors didn't torture, rape,
    and chain a quarter of the world?

When you try to claim that English core – that heartwood –
I think of bogs and fens.   A fen nourishes; a bog preserves.
Dredge it and you'll find bodies – teeth and hair
    and leather frightful-perfect,
clothes and jewellery set in place,
                        the wounds that killed them open still.
You cannot scour their skin to vellum
                    and chart on it some unbroken family line
that makes their world less alien,
    enfolds it in to your imagined noble past.

Botanists will tell you: heartwood is already dead, its purpose served –
rotting sets it free. It turns back into earth,
    feeds the roots it sprang from.
A bog preserves; a fen nourishes   with decomposing plants
and constant water flow from *somewhere else.*
We could scrabble in the mire for long-dead kings to resurrect –
or we could see abundance in decay,
            and let the fantasy of England *rot.*

Hindsight

Sharon Phillips

Ich will wirken in dieser Zeit – Käthe Kollwitz, 1922

It might as well be the 1920s *&* a man
on the street bellowing the end is nigh,
given how weird things have turned,

what with those thugs *&* dupes who
dream about the hordes of barbarians
besieging our gates, the paedophiles
governing the whole world in secret.

Her mission might look as clear today
as it did a century back: she thought
her art could make a difference

to the homeless lads with shell shock,
people starving to feed their children,
the unemployed *&* the sick. Instead
they dreamt of a thousand year Reich.

Race Card

Simon Mansfield

I pulled out me race card,
'Don't persecute me.'

'That's just blank mate,
nothing to see.'

'Exactly,' I said.
'That's the way it should be.

Years of white privilege
have set me free.'

On This Occasion

William Thirsk-Gaskill

I applied for a job on Monday. I had to check a box that said I was eligible to work in the United Kingdom.

I applied for two jobs on Tuesday. I had to check a box that said I had experience of working with the General Data Protection Regulation, and provide a scanned copy of my driving licence.

I applied for three jobs on Wednesday. I had to check a box that said neither I nor any member of my family was currently employed by the Civil Service, provide a scanned copy of my passport, and compose a five-minute presentation on the life cycle of fleas.

I applied for four jobs on Thursday. I had to check a box that said I had experience of managing annual budgets over fifty thousand pounds in value, provide scanned copies of all my examination certificates, compose a ten-minute presentation on the South Sea Bubble, and give an undertaking that I was willing to commute to Birkenhead, five days a week.

I applied for five jobs on Friday. I had to check a box which said that I had no unspent criminal convictions, outstanding county court judgements, and was willing to undergo a full disclosure search for my criminal record, provide scanned copies of my parents' birth certificates, compose a fifteen-minute presentation on the life of Andy Warhol, give an undertaking that I was willing to commute to Folkestone, six days a week, and undergo a full medical.

I applied for six jobs on Saturday. I had to check a box which said that I had never lied, stolen, nor made anyone cry, provide a scanned copy of everything I was thinking at that moment, compose a twenty-minute presentation that would make every member of the audience enjoy every presentation they would ever experience again, as long as they lived, give an undertaking that I was willing to commute to Murmansk, seven days a week, undergo interrogation under conditions of complete sensory deprivation, and agree to go back in time and attempt to assassinate Hitler.

I slept in on Sunday, read a book, watched a film.

On Monday, I was summoned to the Job Centre to hear a lecture on the importance of undertaking job-seeking activities every day. They terminated my claim.

What Remains

Wes Lee

Ellen Ripley dunking a basketball. Her taut, sinewy body. Her face
like my mother's.
At night a yellow plough with flashing lights –
the scar an ambulance drives through your life.
Having to get so shit-faced drunk when I came home.
   The moment I would
roar toward.
And Marie told me don't think about them,
don't let them take your life.
I wanted to wake you to tell you I heard her voice speaking
   in the dream.
And I wonder if I will always be on edge, trying to pull
   some ground my way.
A perfect afternoon where you brought out the lounger chair.
Weeding in the sun after days of pain.
A dog bounding toward me wet from the sea.
Coral at night, pulsing, pulsing. Stringing out its polyps
   in an epic battleground.
Sparing others their discomfort; mirroring their reflections
   to keep myself safe.
Feeling the time bomb.
If I die. I say it a lot, *If I die.*
Dexter rolling the father off the boat saying, 'Bye Daddio!'
The corridor to that bedroom. The house I most often dream of.
The night a stranger slipped a teddy bear under my arm,
her kindness almost frightening.
The hard-to-remember names of medications.
Can I touch you here? And here? Can I give you an injection?
Last time I met a friend I rubbed my elbows raw with attention.

A woman finding water to drown in –
how this preoccupies as something in reserve,
that option there.
Your grey head disappearing along the part of the street we never walk.
Those empty miles of success.
The nurses' station at midnight –
one of Hopper's islands of light, forever floating.
The flashbacks never cease, they surprise me again
with their core features and subtle changes.
I was happy in Airbnbs when we had no home,
     I was happy with adaptation.
Emergency rooms are the strangest, most lonely places on earth.

Why I Repeatedly Ended Up Sitting on the Floor of the 8.45 a.m. TransPennine Express

Faye Chambers

You spot a free seat.
First Class passengers protest:
'They're *vacant*. Not *free*.'

The Cold Ring

Mia Rayson Regan

A child's bloodshot eyes glisten
on his mother's FaceTime screen
as she takes her final, agonising breath.

A woman in the car park,
slumped over the wheel, fighting to keep her eyelids open
as her husband lies motionless, tangled in plastic tubes.

An old man fighting to raise his arm
as he gasps for his little girl in his grandad's voice,
but no one comes – because no one can.

A doctor with dark rings above his mask,
shrunk in his head like the eyes of a skull,
as he phones a fifth family to tell them that Grandma is dead.

A couple admitted together, matching gold rings,
she fights to live as he fights for life.
Soon she leaves, the warm ring on her left finger,
the cold ring on her right.

Judas

Joseph Blythe

I have drive,
But I cannot steer.
I have dreams,
Yet I cannot sleep.

I have faith,
Though I never pray.
I have a voice,
But I do not speak.

I have a pen,
But I cannot write.
I have words,
But I have no tongue.

And I have eyes,
But I've seen enough.
They have hearts,
But they know not love.

Safety First

Matt Hill

In your box buried deep
enduring life's common terminal prognosis
screen-light and candlelight graze the sides.

We helped you build this.
You remain safe from disease, violence, change:
sterile.

The casket blackens then burns
as you hold the candle to it,
searing, burning, you haul
soil-smeared blisters into daylight.

You are scarred, open to infection,
challenge, new perspectives
for better, for worse.
But this could be living.

Arctic Tern

Rosalind York

The last time we came back,
they didn't stamp your passport
with the triangle that lets you stay,
so you put your money down,
spoke the promise on the card.

> *(the arctic tern
> migrates pole to pole)*

It was one hop in a plane:
home to here. Valentine's day, 1967.
You opened goodbye cards from school.
As your accent softened on British knuckles,
you clung to memory: pop tarts,
the red cardinal.

– I do solemnly and sincerely…
Afterwards, you took a selfie
with a portrait of the Queen.

> *(borderless on its raft of sky)*

And that's that. You're one of us.
Outside a bar in Leeds, we pour mojitos
and it starts to rain.

Yorkshire Cricket

Aamina Khan

Job-snatching, brown-skinned immigrant,
taxi-driving, barely-surviving,
broken English, gets you mithering.
Paki is a problem that neither left nor right can fix.
EDL crying: 'get rid, get rid, get rid.'
Paki ain't pale, Paki dunt eat pig, Paki dunt drink, Paki dunt show skin,
but Paki is fast, Paki knows how to pitch.
You can't tell why you hate Paki.
Is it his faith or the colour of his skin?
You'd say: 'Oh well, same thing.
Only banter,' you insist.
Paki can't bend his bones to fit in boxes,
Paki sticks out like a sore gun,
Paki is a parasite that just won't budge,
no matter how hard you shove, shove, shove.
Paki bleeds the same red you smear on your face
when you chant 'Barmy Army'.
Paki breaks his legs to give you World Cup.
Paki catch ball, but can't catch a hint.
We need your pace, we need that six, giz a spin,
juice you dry until we win;
then send you packing to the same borders we snipped.
No matter how many times you testify,
'I was born here,' it dunt change the fact that
Paki ain't pale, Paki dunt eat pig, Paki dunt drink, Paki dunt show skin.

Apocalypse (Synopsis)

Geraldine Clarkson

A thousand starlings plop like gobs of tar
from corned-beef skies, for no apparent cause.
Then fish, with twisted fins, and six-inch scars,
turn up in private gardens and offshore.
Domestic pets climb rooftops late at night
and yowl, as if, despite themselves, they felt
the pull of iron in their bloody bite –
a rankle or an itch below the pelt.
Grand beasts, like tigers, amble with their cubs
to play with ducklings fledging in the park;
soft-sheathe their claws behind the flower tubs;
excel at karaoke after dark.
Two-headed babies grizzle at the breast.
And tabloid hacks keep *schtum* – 'it's for the best'.

Two Minutes in Translation

Suna Afshan

Gujar Khan, Pakistan

Mohammed Yasin!
                    Oh!
Hello, my child!
                    [My lamb, my son!]
I yearn for you so dearly.
        [And I'm so full of fire!]
Oh, my child, I'm so full of longing's fire,
Oh, my Mohammed Yasin!
Oh, my son, I'm so full of fire.
Oh, my Mohammed Yasin,
When will you come home?

        And my lovely lamb, my Amjid,
You who were torn from my embrace!
[You, who my eyes have forgotten.]
My child, I'm missing you so much;
I'm so worried – *oh!* – my child,
When will I ever see you again?
        Because, my Mohammed Yasin,
My heart's a fragile flower!
So this I pray never happens:
That I die without
Setting my eyes on you again.
Oh, the hardships – *painful*
Hardships – I've paid. Oh!
Child of mine, if you knew …

And oh, my child,
May God give you so much life!
My sons, the prayers prayed for you at all hours –
With every namaz I pray:
God, may my children not want for anything,
For such is your mercy, your grace.
God, where have my children gone,
[And to which country have you taken them?]
And upon each rosary bead,
One pure, holy book,
[For my sins, and for my sorrow].

And oh, my lambs, I'm feeble.
I'm in pain [and this pain is so tough],
It's leeched me of my strength –
This is not some mind-born delusion!
The truth is, my heart is weak,
So, at every moment, I want
My Amjid to be near;
That I may gaze upon him;
That I may speak to him again.

And the other thing is that ...
For me, [your ailing father]
Won't you read a prayer?
My child – *though only God knows* –
One day [and just once],
I wish for us two to meet again.
    That's it.
For that meeting, I'd like you to pray.

Because my child
[My children, my sons],
Had I known that
It would be the last one ...

Come a little closer.
Sit a little closer
To the microphone.

And the final thing is –
For God Almighty's sake
– If you are to come
Mohammed Yasin,
Bring my Amjid
With you to visit,
Do not come to me alone.

Asylum

Jack Faricy

To the natives, Hartshead Moor evokes
the vividly imagined landscapes
of Yorkshire's famous Brontë sisters,
or Robin Hood's fellowship
of merry-making outlaws, or the pluck
and tenacity of Luddite rebels, or
the exceptional levels of customer satisfaction
recorded for eleven years running
at the M62's premier service station.
This is where your journey will end
and the shutters be raised
on a bright new dawn as the sun lifts
over ancient Elmet and casts
its golden glow over your future
as British citizens enjoying
your right to remain, your cash allowance,
your somewhere to live
in Batley, Dewsbury, Oldham, Rochdale
or any of the Northern Powerhouse's
regenerated mill towns strung
along the TransPennine motorway
like pearls on a necklace,
and sharing our fundamental values
of democracy, the rule of law, individual
liberty, and mutual respect for
and tolerance of those with different
faiths and beliefs and those
without faith.

Contributors

Suna Afshan is the Editor of Pallina Press, Co-founder and Editor at Large at *Poetry Birmingham*, and is on the Editorial Board of Broken Sleep Books. Her work has appeared in *The TLS*, *Modern Poetry in Translation*, *The London Magazine*, *Stand*, *Magma*, and others. Suna's debut is the micro-pamphlet *Belladonna*, a long poem published by Legitimate Snack (2020).

Gary Allen was born in Ballymena, Co. Antrim. He has published nineteen collections, most recently, *Bonfire Night*, Greenwich Exchange Publishing. Highly commended in the Forward Prize 2019. Widely published in magazines, including: *London Magazine*, *The New Statesman*, *Poetry Review*, *Stand*, *The Wild Court*.

Joe Allen was born in Ballymena, Co. Antrim. He has published six collections, most recently, *Clabber Street Blues*, Greenwich Exchange Publishing. Published widely in magazines: *Agenda*, *London Magazine*, *Stand*, etc. He is also a performing Delta Blues Singer, Guitarist and Harmonica player. He is a brother of Gary Allen.

Nick Allen has published one collection and three pamphlets of poetry: the most recent being a limited edition – all proceeds to the NHS – *Morphine Bone Dream*.

Jimmy Andrex co-founded Red Shed Readings, makes radio for ELFM and has been on BBC 6 Music. Last summer he performed *Stupidity is Not The Problem* and *Billy Baggins There and Back*, a modern adaptation of *The Hobbit*. Recently, he wrote and performed *Tree Talk* for Wakefield Word Fest.

Ben Banyard lives in Portishead on the Severn Estuary near Bristol. His third collection of poetry, *Hi-Viz*, was published by Yaffle Press in 2021. Ben edits *Black Nore Review* and blogs at benbanyard.wordpress.com.

Bob Beagrie lives in Middlesbrough and has published numerous collections of poetry and several pamphlets, most recently: *When We Wake We Think We're Whalers from Eden* (Stairwell Books 2021); *And Then We Saw The Daughter of the Minotaur* (The Black Light Engine Press 2020); *Civil Insolencies* (Smokestack 2019).

Penny Blackburn lives in the North East of England but is originally from Yorkshire. Her poetry has been published by, among others, *Poetry Society News, Atrium, Phare, Riggwelter*, and *Fly on the Wall*. She has recently been commended in the Waltham Forest and Positive Images Festival competitions.

Joseph Blythe is a 22-year-old writer of prose and poetry from Yorkshire. Having written since a young age, he has never had any doubt about what he wants to do with his life and often finds himself writing too much and studying too little.

After being homeless in her teens, Cathy Bryant worked as a life model, shoe shop assistant, civil servant and childminder before writing professionally. She has won 29 literary awards and her work has been published all over the world.

Anne Caldwell is a poet and Royal Literary Fund Fellow at the University of Huddersfield. She is also a lecturer in Creative Writing for the Open University. She has published four collections of poetry including *Alice and the North* (Valley Press, 2020). She edited *The Valley Press Anthology of Prose Poetry* with Oz Hardwick.

Gerry Cambridge has published six collections since 1995, including *Aves*, prose poems on wild birds (Essence Press, 2007); *Notes for Lighting a Fire* (HappenStance, 2012); and *The Light Acknowledgers & Other*

Poems (HappenStance, 2019). In 1995 he founded, and still edits, *The Dark Horse*, Scotland's foremost magazine of poetry and criticism.

Kayleigh Campbell is a member of the Editorial Board for Grist and a Creative Writing PhD candidate at the University of Huddersfield. Her debut poetry collection *Matryoshka* is due April 2022 from Verve Poetry Press. Her work has appeared in *Butcher's Dog*, *The Rialto* and *Stand*.

Alberto Fernández Carbajal (he/they) is a Spanish lecturer and writer living in the North of England. They are Senior Lecturer at the University of Roehampton (London), where they teach English and Creative Writing. Their short fiction has appeared in *The View from Here*, *Gay Flash Fiction*, and *Litro*. Their poem '?' has recently been published by *DEFUNKT* and their poem 'sing(e) me' will feature in the seminal issue of the new journal *Queer Aesthetics*. Alberto lives on the border between Yorkshire and Lancashire with their civil partner, their son, three cats, a whippet, and around two dozen goldfish.

Faye Chambers is a 27-year-old writer, musician and linguist from Elland, West Yorkshire. She is currently studying for a PhD in the Language of Humour at the University of Huddersfield. In between lurking in guitar shops and investigating dirty jokes you can find her at afayewithwords.wordpress.com.

Geraldine Clarkson's poems have appeared in *The Poetry Review*, *Mslexia*, *Magma* (Selected Poet), *The Dark Horse* and *Poetry magazine*. Her first poetry pamphlet was a PBS Pamphlet Choice, and her second was a Laureate's Choice. Her most recent publications are *Monica's Overcoat of Flesh* (Nine Arches, 2020) and *Crucifox* (Verve Poetry Press, 2021).

Mark Connors is a poet, novelist and Creative Writing Tutor from Leeds. His third poetry collection, *After* is out now through YAFFLE PRESS. He is currently hard at work on his third novel and a hybrid book of prose and poetry called *2022*. For more info visit markconnors.co.uk.

Ian Duhig has won the Forward Best Poem Prize once and the National Poetry Competition twice. His *New and Selected Poems* was a Poetry Book Society Special Commendation, an Irish Times Poetry Book of the Year, a *Guardian* Poetry Book of the Year and an Observer Book of the Year for 2021.

Glyn Edwards is a PhD researcher in ecopoetry at Bangor University. His first poetry collection *Vertebrae* is published by the Lonely Press, *In Orbit* is forthcoming with Seren. He is a trustee of the Terry Hetherington Award for Welsh young writers, and works as a teacher in North Wales.

Steve Ely is a poet and novelist. He teaches Creative Writing at the University of Huddersfield, where he is also Director of the Ted Hughes Network. His most recent books are *Lectio Violant* and *The European Eel*.

Jack Faricy is a poet and English teacher who is studying for a PhD in Creative Writing at the University of Huddersfield. He is working on a series of poems exploring the M62 and the landscapes it connects/divides. His first collection, *Traces*, is published by Calder Valley Poetry.

Kerry Featherstone has been published and given readings in France, Germany, India, Romania and the UK. He writes poetry and songs – in French and English – often about the relationship between history, memory, people and place. He is a Lecturer in Creative Writing at Loughborough University and supports emerging writers.

Betsie Flynn is a Kentish transplant to the Brecon Beacons where she lives with her husband, children, and cats.

Jim Greenhalf's poems don't tick boxes: they knock them or mock them. Redbeck Press and Smokestack Books account for most of his thirteen books of poems. Some are in ten anthologies published by, among others, Random House, The Wilfred Owen Society and Grist. 'Remembrance Sunday' was performed by Huddersfield University drama students during the centenary of World War One.

Robin Gurney is a writer, performer, and avid researcher. Fascinated by the liminal and monstrous, Robin finds inspiration in folklore, nature, and their own queerness and disability. Selected past works and current projects, from Old English translation soundscapes to a full-length Fringe show, are catalogued at robinredhood.carrd.co.

Atar Hadari's *Songs from Bialik: Selected Poems of H. N. Bialik* (Syracuse University Press) was a finalist for the American Literary Translators' Association Award and his debut collection, *Rembrandt's Bible*, was published by Indigo Dreams in 2013. *Lives of the Dead: Poems of Hanoch Levin* won a Pen Translates award and is out now from Arc Publications.

Ashley Hickson-Lovence is a novelist currently completing his PhD in Creative Writing at the University of East Anglia. His debut novel *The 392* was released in 2019 and his second novel *Your Show*, based on the life and career of former football referee Uriah Rennie, will be released in April 2022.

Kevin Higgins was born in London and lives in Galway, Ireland. In 2016 *The Stinging Fly* magazine described Kevin as 'likely the most read living poet in Ireland'. He has published five poetry collections, and a New & Selected, with Salmon Poetry. His sixth collection *Ecstatic* is published in March.

After attending Michael Stewart's Invisible Writers Group in 2017 Matt Hill collaborated on Leeds Lit Fest 2019's Tweeting a Tale for Found Fiction. The same year he had 'Losing Control' published in *Trouble: Grist Anthology Of Protest – Short Stories*. 'Safety First' is Matt's first published poem.

Georgia Hilton is an Irish poet and fiction writer, now living in Winchester, England. Her work has appeared in magazines such as *The Rialto*, *Prole Magazine*, *192 Magazine*, and *Perhappened*. Georgia is the author of two books of poetry, both published by Dempsey and Windle. She is married with three children.

Natalie Ann Holborow is author of *And Suddenly You Find Yourself and Small* (Parthian) and co-author of *The Wrong Side of the Looking Glass* (Black Rabbit Press). She currently works in marketing and is both the editor of the Cheval anthology and a proud patron of the Leon Heart Fund.

Gaia Holmes is the author of three poetry collections, *Dr James Graham's Celestial Bed*, *Lifting The Piano With One Hand* and *Where The Road Runs Out*. All published by Comma Press. She is a writing tutor and pet/house sitter and lives in Halifax in a tiny flat above the tree line on the top floor of a ramshackle Georgian mansion. She is currently working on her debut collection of short stories.

Jennifer Johnson was born in Sudan, spent part of her childhood in Ghana and later worked as a VSO agriculturalist in Zambia. Widely published in magazines (most recently in *Stand*) and anthologies, her work includes *Footprints on Africa and Beyond* (Hearing Eye, 2006) and *Hints and Shadows* (Nettle Press, 2017).

Aamina Khan is an aspiring spoken word poet from Halifax. She has a strong passion for writing things that challenge and open people's minds. She tends to write poems based on spirituality, body image and identity.

Safia Khan is a poet and medical student. She is a winner of the New Poets Prize 2021; her debut collection is due for publication in 2022 (Smith | Doorstop). Her poetry has been published in *The North*, *BATH MAGG*, *Poetry Wales*, *Introduction X: The Poetry Business Book of New Poets* and several Hive anthologies.

Originally from Burnley, Wes Lee lives in New Zealand. Her latest poetry collection, *By the Lapels*, was launched in 2019. Most recently she was awarded the *Poetry New Zealand* Prize 2019 by Massey University Press, and shortlisted for The NZSA Laura Solomon Cuba Press Prize 2021. She is the featured poet in the *Poetry New Zealand* Yearbook 2022.

S ann à Leòdhas a tha Pàdraig MacAoidh, agus tha dà leabhar aige le Acair: *Gu Leòr* (2015) agus *Nàdur De* (2020). Tha e' a' fuireach ann an Dun Èideann.

Peter Mackay has two collections with Acair: *Galore* (2015) and *Some Kind of* (2020). Originally from the Isle of Lewis, he now lives in Edinburgh.

MacGillivray is the author of three poetry collections: *The Last Wolf of Scotland* (Red Hen Press), *The Nine of Diamonds: Surroial Mordantless* and *The Gaelic Garden of the Dead* (Bloodaxe Books). Her fourth book *Ravage: An Astonishment of Fire* is published by Bloodaxe in 2023.

Simon Mansfield knows a real poet.

Charlotte Murray is a writer from West Yorkshire. She won second place in Bangor Literary Journal's Forty Words Competition and Lucent Dreaming's Poetry Competition 2021. She has been published in various journals and anthologies, including *CP Quarterly*, *the winnow*, *Mancunian Ways* anthology and *New Beginnings* anthology. Her Twitter is @charlouwriter.

John Newsham's novel, *Killing the Horses*, was published by Wrecking Ball Press in 2021. His short story of the same name was longlisted for the Manchester Fiction Prize. He has won accolades for his poetry and has performed at festivals across the north of England. He lives in West Yorkshire.

Sharon Phillips started writing when she retired. Her poems have appeared in print and online journals and anthologies, including *Places of Poetry*, *Poetry Birmingham*, *Raceme*, *About Larkin*, *The Poetry Society Newsletter*, *Atrium*, *The Clearing*, *Ink Sweat and Tears*, *The High Window* and *The Friday Poem*.

Mia Rayson Regan is an aspiring young writer from Leeds and is currently studying English Literature with Creative Writing at the University of Huddersfield. She was diagnosed with type one diabetes at eighteen but uses the challenges with her disability to craft and develop her writing.

Michael Stewart's debut novel, *King Crow*, was the winner of the *Guardian*'s Not-the-Booker Award. Other books include *Couples*; *Café Assassin*; *Mr Jolly*, and *Ill Will: The Untold Story of Heathcliff*. *Walking the Invisible*, a hybrid memoir about the Brontës' lives and landscapes, was published by HarperCollins in June 2021. He is also the creator of the Brontë Stones project. michael-stewart.org.uk.

Joelle Taylor is the author of four collections of poetry. Her newest collection *C+NTO & Othered Poems* (June 2021) was awarded the T.S Eliot Prize and was the subject of a Radio 4 arts documentary, *Butch*. She is a co-curator and host of Out-Spoken Live, resident at the Southbank Centre, and the current editor of Out-Spoken Press.

William Thirsk-Gaskill was born in Leeds in 1967. He and his wife, Valerie, appeared in a joint performance at Wakefield Litfest 2017, called *Welcome To The Mad*. William's adaptation of his Grist novella, *Escape Kit*, was broadcast by BBC Radio 4 in 2019. His collections of poetry and short fiction are available from stairwellbooks.co.uk.

South London born, Dave Wakely has worked as a musician, university administrator, poetry librarian and editor. His writing has appeared in *Ambit*, *Fictive Dream*, *Glitterwolf*, *Mechanics' Institute Review*, *The Phare*, *Prole*, *Shooter* and *Token*, amongst others. Co-organiser of Milton Keynes Literature Festival, he lives in Buckinghamshire.

Rory Waterman's full-length collections, all published by Carcanet, are: *Tonight the Summer's Over* (2013, PBS Recommendation, shortlisted for a Seamus Heaney Award); *Sarajevo Roses* (2017, shortlisted for Ledbury Forte Prize); and *Sweet Nothings* (2020). He also wrote *Brexit Day on the Balmoral Estate* (Rack, 2017). He is on the English faculty at NTU.

Ben Willems lives in Manchester and has been writing and performing poetry for nearly 20 years. His writing is inspired by political slapstick, social static, internet traffic, re-arranging Titanic deckchair levels of internal head clatter. He has been published by *Some Roast Poet*, *The Recusant*, *Beatification*, and *Citizen 32* among others.

Gregory Woods is the author of six poetry collections from Carcanet Press, the latest being *Records of an Incitement to Silence* (2021). His main books on gay cultural history are published by Yale University Press. He is Emeritus Professor of Gay and Lesbian Studies at Nottingham Trent University.

Rosalind York read Theatre at Dartington and has won prizes in the York Open and the Guernsey International Poetry Competition. Her pamphlet, *The Flank of a Fish*, came out in 2015 and her collection, *The Taste of Red* in 2020.

Acknowledgements

The Grist editorial board would first like to thank our two main supporters: The University of Huddersfield, and Arts Council England. Grist Books was established in 2009 by writer Michael Stewart, who is Head of Creative Writing at The University of Huddersfield. Grist produces publications that bring together established and new writers in order to promote the careers of emerging writers. Grist is more than just the in-house publication of the University of Huddersfield's Creative Writing department: it aims to bring new writing and new writing opportunities to diverse audiences. Writers who were first published by Grist have gone on to become big names in the world of literature. None of what has been achieved so far could have happened without the continuing support of the university. In addition to this ongoing support, in the summer of 2021 we were lucky to secure funding from Arts Council England that has enabled us to publish this anthology, as well as a number of other related initiates, that will help us to promote new writing. We were mentored and advised in this application by Stephen May, to who we owe our gratitude. Grist is a core team of Michael Stewart, Steve Ely and Kayleigh Campbell. In addition, we are helped and assisted by a large student team. The current team is: Aamina Khan, Aimie Allen, Alicia Peal, Alix Luxton, Amir Khan, Bethany Howlett, Briony Sanderson, Danielle Farr, Eleanor Fisher, Ellen Clarke, Habiba Desai, Haleema Ahmed, Hannah Holmes, Jack Leader, Jessica Westhead, Khazir Abbas, Lucy Lunney-Milner, Mia Rayson Regan, Rebecca Young, Rhiannon Randall, Robyn Copeland, Samuel Higson-Blythe, Syed Idrees, Zahra Hafejee. The Grist editorial board would like to extend our thanks to this student team and in particular Samuel Higson-Blythe.